Microsoft Excel Exercises For Everyone

Exercises for Microsoft Office Excel

Authored by:

Mark Gillan MBCS MCMI MIFP MILT TQFE

Microsoft Excel Exercises For Everyone

Mark Gillan

Member of the British Computer Society

Further and Higher Education College Lecturer

Teacher Qualified (Further Education)

Microsoft Certified Trainer

Member of the Chartered Institute of Logistics & Transport

Member of the Institute of Freight Professionals

Professional Photographer and Artist

Accredited Microsoft Certified Application Specialist

Certified Internet Webmaster

Member: Chartered Management Institute

Skoosh Media Ltd

Registered in Scotland

A copy of this book has been made available to:
The British Library, London, England

Registered in Scotland SC226730

www.SkooshMedia.com

Author: Mark Gillan

Publisher: Skoosh Media Ltd

ISBN: 978-0-9557770-7-3

For Lisa and Melissa, my friends and family,

and visually impaired people around the world.

Target Audience

Businesses

Any organisation wishing to gauge employee skills or assess prospective employees

Individuals

Personal learning through exercise completion, video demonstration and viewing final files

Academics

Educationalists around the world may wish to purchase or recommend the purchase of this book for their students. This book provides an excellent ready made classroom resource with video demonstrations and answer files for checking or marking

Learners

Students for an easier way to learn

Trainers

HR office or training establishment for each trainee

Home Users

The home user wishing to use Microsoft Office Excel for personal finance planning or just to realise the fantastic possibilities within your computer

Career Minded

Anyone wanting to succeed with computers and find a new job, whether bored in current job, made redundant or seeking employment for any other reason

Everyone!

Foreword

It is not until we are shown or come across a different situation that we understand how much we have still to learn.

We are all learners.

The exercises begin at an earlier stage of use and develop as you work your way through. May I advise readers to perform every step of every exercise with an open mind, acknowledging your knowledge may be lacking in some areas and surprising yourself during your travel through the book. Use the CD-ROM to view video tutorials, noting they may differ to your own, with new techniques and processes being on show. Reinforce your current ability, refresh forgotten areas, learn new commands, recognise requirements for progression and more importantly enjoy the book.

Each exercise commences at the top of a new page, pleasantly spaced within the margins and efficiently numbered for your convenience. I have taken into consideration my own personal likes and dislikes of professional books read over the years.

Lessons to which I am in front of students always commence with me reminding all learners, we all make mistakes. I encourage students to inform me when they slip-up. Most lessons take a slightly different route due to a diverse group or individual thinking totally dissimilar to the previous class group. Mistakes remind me to show students how to handle errors, with demonstrations of typical mishaps occurring and sorting immediately without embarrassment, frustration, fuss or thinking they are in isolation. Throughout the video demonstrations on the CD-ROM accompanying this book, I show some typing errors as well as possible misdirection or pitfalls. I admit to being sneaky with students, teaching technique without them realising they have received additional knowledge, meaning they continue with good confidence. All learners should keep confidence, enjoy learning and appreciate the incredible workings of Microsoft Office.

My enthusiasm for technology is nearly as strong as my intent to help others.

Ever since a child, I have wanted to help others, it is an obsession in a way. Writing this book is just one further step to helping people around the world, whether businesses, individuals, students, educators or charities.

Charitable organisations working with sight impairment have always been close to my heart, as has teaching. The purpose of writing this book was to help Microsoft Office Excel users around the world in conjunction with contributing part of any profits to charity.

My next book will be Microsoft Office Word Exercises for Everyone, providing learning opportunities and a testing environment. Thereafter, a more advanced Microsoft Office Excel book is definitely an option.

With the majority of people using their computer as a glorified typewriter and businesses unaware their employees have some necessary skills but lack development, it is apparent books enhancing every Microsoft Office user's knowledge are required.

If someone continually swims across a river without ever seeing a boat or being told of the use of boats, how would they ever understand how much quicker it would be to get to the other side?

You don't know the enormous benefits of computing until you are shown or identify new tools. Hopefully I can help.

Thanks and best regards to all,

The Start

Each exercise is self sufficient and does not rely upon any actions from previous chapters.

All the files needed to perform exercises reside within the TexQuest folder on the CD-ROM cited upon the inside of the back cover.

You will be requested to save files at the end of each exercise into the TexAns folder. You can either create this folder yourself on your own PC or copy the folder along with the TexQuest folder.

Remember, only 1 PC at any time can hold folders and files from the CD-ROM per 1 licence. The easy explanation is: 1 user per 1 licence. Discounts may be available for large quantities of books / licences, please enquire. Also remember, part of any profits from these books will be donated to charity, so it is not just a legal responsibility but a friendly request.

Video animation of the answers are provided within the Video folder on the CD-ROM.

Files showing the final answers are available within the Final folder on the CD-ROM. These files along with the video answer files can be used to either learn or for marking by an assessor or teacher.

The list of exercises and page numbers is available at the back of the book. It was best to let you start rather than put all the content data padding the front of the book. I am sure you want to get started.

>>> COPY TexQuest and TexAns folders from the CD-ROM onto your own PC's local drive

Exercise 1

New File, Inserting content, Saving, Exiting

1.　Run Microsoft Office Excel

2.　Within Cell A1 of the new workbook, type: New One

3.　Navigate to cell P180, type: Here

4.　Save the file to the **TexAns** folder and name the file: **First1**

5.　Exit Microsoft Office Excel

Exercise 2

Opening, Editing, Saving, Closing, Exiting

1. Run Microsoft Office Excel

2. From the TexQuest folder, open the file: **Exer2**

3. Edit Cell A1 to read: Mark

4. Navigate to cell AK25, delete the contents

5. Save the file to the **TexAns** folder and name the file: **Second2**

6. Close the file

7. Request a blank new workbook

8. Within Cell A1 of the new workbook, type: Another1

9. Save the file to the TexAns folder and name the file: **Second2a**

10. Close the file and exit Microsoft Office Excel

Exercise 3

Opening, Editing, Printing, Saving, Exiting

1. Run Microsoft Office Excel

2. Open the workbook file from the TexQuest folder named: **messages**

3. Delete the contents of cell D1

4. Change Cell A8 to read: Well Fired Rolls

5. Change the unit price of the Well Fired Rolls to read: £0.57

6. Change Cell A12 from Carrots to read: Brussel Sprouts

7. Change the quantity of Newspaper from 1 to 3

8. Enter the following into Cell A25: Checklist

9. Save the file as a workbook with the file name as **messages3** into the TexAns folder.

10. Print 2 copies of the spreadsheet to your nearest printer.

11. Exit Microsoft Office Excel.

Exercise 4

Opening, Editing, Saving, More Editing, Saving

1.   Run Microsoft Office Excel

2.   Open the workbook file from the TexQuest folder named:
     homeoffice

3.   Change Cell A5 to read: Staple dispenser

4.   Change the unit price of the Staple dispenser from £5.52 to
     read: £10.99

5.   Save the file as a workbook with the file name as
     homeoffice4 into the **TexAns** folder.

6.   Change Cell A12 from A3 writing pad to read: A4 notepad

7.   Change the quantity of USB Flash Drive from 3 to 5

8.   Input your name into cell A27

9.   Save the file as a workbook with the file name as
     homeoffice4a into the **TexAns** folder.

10.   Exit Microsoft Office Excel.

Exercise 5

Opening, Editing, Replacing / Saving, Exiting

1. Run Microsoft Office Excel

2. Open the workbook file from the **TexQuest** folder named: **Towns**

3. Change Cell A13 to read: 3901 Seville

4. Save the file as a workbook with the file name as: **NewTown5** into the **TexAns** folder

5. Close the file but keep Microsoft Office Excel running

6. Request a brand new blank workbook

7. In cell A1 type: Lottery List

8. In cell A2 type: FirstName

9. Save the file as a workbook with the file name as: **Lottery5** within the TexAns folder

10. Close the file but keep Microsoft Office Excel running

11. Open the workbook file from the TexAns folder named: **NewTown5**

12. Change Cell A12 to read: 3801 Cardinal Cove

13. Save the file as a workbook with the file name as: **NewTown5** (replacing the file) in the TexAns folder

14. Close any open workbook files

Exercise 6

Summary test: Opening, Editing, Saving, Printing

1. Open the worksheet file from the TexQuest folder named: **homeofficeb**

2. Change Cell A18 to read: Laser Printer

3. Change the unit price of the Laser Printer from £75.00 to read: £298.50

4. Change Cell A11 from Marker Pen to read: Permanent Marker Pen

5. Change the quantity of Staples from 5 to 27

6. Input your name into cell A33

7. Print 3 copies of the worksheet to your nearest printer

8. Save the file as a workbook with the file name as: **homeoffice6** within the **TexAns** folder

9. Close all open files

Exercise 7

Summary 2: Opening, Editing, Saving, Printing

1. Open the workbook file from the TexQuest folder named: **messagesb**

2. Change Cell A10 to read: Cooking Apples

3. Change the contents of cell D1 to now read: Listing

4. Change the unit price of the Newspaper to read: £0.79

5. Change Cell A16 to read: Semi Skimmed Milk

6. Change the quantity of Pasta Shapes from 3 to 47

7. Enter your name into Cell A30

8. Print 4 copies of the spreadsheet to your nearest printer

9. Save the file as a workbook with the file name as: **messages7** within the **TexAns** folder

10. Close all open files

Exercise 8

Open, Print Selection Only, Save

1. Open the workbook file from the TexQuest folder named: **First2008**

2. Print the January values for Banana and Apple only, setting the print area for this range of cells, as per the

	January
Banana	33.00
Apple	29.80

example shown:

3. Save the file as a workbook with the file name as: **JanOnly8** within the **TexAns** folder

4. Close any open workbook files

Exercise 9

Navigate sheets, Print Selection, Save

1. Open the workbook file from the TexQuest folder named: **ClassExam1**

2. Within the same file, navigate to the worksheet named: IT_Only

3. Print the heading of Student plus the list of names without the IT mark, setting the print area to ensure this data is the only data printed at any point in the future

4. Navigate back to the sheet named: Exams

5. Change the IT result for Mary Smith to read: 7

6. Change the name of Mary Smith to now read: Mary Niven

7. Save the file as a workbook with the file name as: **Class9** within the **TexAns** folder

8. Print 2 copies of the area previously set for printing purposes

9. Close any open workbook files

Exercise 10

Column Width, Basic Cell Formatting, Create new sub folder, Save to new subfolder

1. Open the workbook file from the TexQuest folder named: **Shop4**

2. Alter the width of Column A to: 20.00 point (165 pixels)

3. Alter the width of Columns C and D to accommodate the contents of each of the columns

4. Make the contents of row 3 embolden and underlined

5. Make the contents of cells A12:A17 italic

6. Make the Grand Total value in cell D20 the colour red for its font

7. Increase the size of font for cell A1 to 20 point and bold

8. Change the font for cell D20 to Comic Sans or Tahoma

9. Save the file as a workbook with the file name as: **Shop10** within a new folder you are to create within the **TexAns** folder. Name the new folder: **Sub1**

10. Ensure you have saved the file into the newly created folder , then close all open files.

Exercise 11

Copying and Moving cell contents

1. Open the workbook file from the TexQuest folder named: **Cars09**

2. Navigate to the worksheet within this file named: **Tenth**

3. Move the contents of cells A1 and A2, namely: George and Jane, and place the contents in cells E5 and E7 respectively

4. Navigate to the worksheet named: **August**

5. Copy the contents of the date and cars sold, including the headers, for the date of: 10/08/2009. The contents should be copied to the worksheet named: **Tenth** starting at cell A1

6. From the worksheet named: **Cars**, copy all the Sales ID data to the worksheet named: **SalesID**, starting at cell A1

7. Within the worksheet named: Cars, move the contents of cell G1 to occupy H1 instead

8. Save the file as a workbook with the file name as: **CarsSold11** within the **TexAns** folder

9. Close all open workbooks

Exercise 12

Entering data, Basic Formulae

1.   Create a blank new worksheet

2.   In cell A1, enter: Female

3.   In cell A2, enter: Male

4.   In cell A3, enter: Total Population

5.   In cell B1, enter: 450

6.   In cell B2, enter: 320

7.   In cell B3, enter a simple formula for adding Female and Male to attain a total population value

8.   Save the file as a workbook with the file name as: **Pop12** within the **TexAns** folder

9.   Close all open workbooks

Exercise 13

More Basic Formulae

1. Open the workbook file from the TexQuest folder named: **simform**

2. In cell B3, insert a simple formula to add the amount for Mary with the amount for Paul for the total amount

3. In cell E3, insert a simple formula to add the amount for Jack with the amount for Jill to provide the total amount

4. In cell A18 enter: 5

5. In cell B18 enter: 10

6. In cell C18, insert a simple formula to multiply out the quantity by the unit price to ascertain the total

7. Edit cell E2 to now read: 500

8. Save the file as a workbook with the file name as: **simform13** within the **TexAns** folder

9. Close all open files

Exercise 14

Even More Basic Formulae

1. Open the workbook file from the TexQuest folder named: **Exer14**

2. In cell B3, insert a simple formula to deduct the discount amount from the RRP amount to allocate the actual sales amount

3. Edit the RRP amount to show: £15,235.11

4. Save the file as a workbook with the file name as: **Exer14total** within the **TexAns** folder

5. Close all open files

Exercise 15

Editing Basic Formulae

1. Open the workbook file from the TexQuest folder named: **Exer15**

2. Cell B5 has an error within the formula and does not calculate a quarter of the Annual Revenue, correct the formula to use the correct operator to show an amount per quarter. The operator is the only edit required to remedy the calculation

3. Cell B17 contains a formula referring to incorrect cells, adjust the formula to correctly identify the difference between years 2008 and 2009

4. Save the file as a workbook with the file name as: **Exer15fix** within the **TexAns** folder

5. Close all open files

Exercise 18

Series fill, fill handle and copy

1. Request a blank new workbook

2. In cell A1, enter the word: Date

3. In cell A2, type date: 1/1/09

4. Using series fill, from cell A2 down to cell A13, insert the 1st day of every month up until December of the year 2009

5. In cell B1, enter the word: Packages

6. Starting in cell B2 with the value of 5, using series fill input increments of 5 until cell B13 containing the value of 60

7. In cell C1, enter the word: Destination

8. In cell C2, enter the name Australia and using series fill copy the contents of the cell down to cell C13

9. In cell D1, enter the word: Month

10. In cell D2, enter the month: January

11. Series fill the month from cell D2 down to cell D13 so the months range from January to December, with December occupying cell D13

12. Save the file as a workbook with the file name as: **Series18** within the **TexAns** folder

13. Close all open files

Exercise 19

Basic Formulae and Series Fill Summary

1. Open the workbook file from the TexQuest folder named: **Revenue**

2. In cells of column A under the Date heading, insert the 1st day of every month for the year 2009, ending in cell A13

3. In cells of column B under the Manager heading, for each of the cells down to and including cell B13, the name: John McGhee

4. In cells of column C under the Sales heading, for each of the cells down to and including cell C13, enter the value of: 250

5. In cell D2 enter the value: 1.50 and in cell D3 enter the value: 2.00 and increase the amounts by 0.50 for each cell down to and including cell D13

6. In cell C17 enter a formula calculating the difference between the year sales of 2008 and 2009

7. In cell C20 enter a formula calculating the carried surplus plus the 2009 total sales value

8. In cell C23, enter a formula calculating the tax for 2009 total sales based upon the percentage noted in cell C22

9. Setting the print areas and printing 2 copies of the range B14:C23, to the nearest printer

10. Save the file as a workbook with the file name as: **Revenue19** within the **TexAns** folder

11. Close all open files

Exercise 16

Intermediate formulae with calculating tax

1. Open the workbook file from the TexQuest folder named: **Tax**

2. In cell G6, enter a formula to calculate the tax amount, using the price and the rate of tax applicable to this particular product

3. In cell H6, enter a formula to total the price and tax to provide a selling price inclusive of tax

4. In cell G7, enter a formula to calculate the tax amount, using the price and the rate of tax applicable to this particular product

5. In cell H7, enter a formula to total the price and tax to provide a selling price inclusive of tax

6. Save the file as a workbook with the file name as: **Tax16** within the **TexAns** folder

7. Close all open files

Exercise 17

More Intermediate formulae with tax calculation

1.   Open the workbook file from the TexQuest folder named:
     Smiles

2.   In cell G10, enter a formula for calculating the price of the
     Scots Smile product considering the quantity

3.   In cell G15, enter a formula for calculating the total price
     including tax at the applicable rate mentioned in cell F12

4.   Save the file as a workbook with the file name as:
     Smiles17 within the **TexAns** folder

5.   Edit the quantity in cell F10 to now read: 750

6.   Save the file using the same file name, destination folder
     and file type

7.   In cell G18, enter a formula for calculating the price of the
     Alba Face product considering the quantity

8.   In cell G23, enter a formula for calculating the total price
     including tax at the applicable rate mentioned in cell F20

9.   Edit the quantity in cell F18 to now read: 3550

10. Save the file using the same file name, destination folder
     and file type

11. Edit the tax rate in cell F20 to now read: 22%

12. Save the file as a workbook with the file name as:
     Smiles17b within the **TexAns** folder

13. Close all open files

Exercise 20

Date / Time Formatting, Copying between sheets

1. Open the workbook file from the TexQuest folder named: **despatch**

2. Within the worksheet named: Europe. Format cells D4:D7 to show long form date, for example: 21 April 2010 (Date, Month, Year) without any change due to regional locality and operating system influence

3. In cells: D4 input: 19/7/2009, D5 input: 22/8/2009, D6 input : 9/10/2009 and in D7 input: 2/11/2009

4. Format cells E4:E7 to show time in 24 hour clock with seconds, without any change due to regional locality and operating system influence

5. In cells: E4 input: 17:23, E5 input: 10:44:55, E6 input: 21:44:12 and in cell E7 input: 00:21:30

6. Format cells F4:F7 to show the date in short form, for example: 12/3/09

7. In cells: F4 input: 20/7/09, F5 input: 23 August 2009, F6 input:: 19 October 2009, and in cell F7 input: 7/11/2009

8. Copy the range of cells D4:F7 and paste the contents and formatting into the same range of cells within the worksheet named: USA

9. Edit all dates within the USA worksheet to show in US locale format in short form, namely: Month, Date, Year. For example: 21 October 2009 must be shown: 10/21/09

10. Save the file as a workbook with the file name as: **despatch20** within the **TexAns** folder

11. Close all open files

Exercise 21

Currency Formatting

1.   Open the workbook file from the TexQuest folder named: **StockSale**

2.   On Sheet 1, cell C2, enter: £12.54

3.   On Sheet 1, cell C3, enter: £9.01

4.   On Sheet 1, cells C4:C7, format the cells for currency to two decimal places

5.   On Sheet 1, cell C4, enter: 1.5 and cell C5 enter: 2.04, cell C6 enter: 1.9 and cell C7 enter: 3.54

6.   Edit cell C3 by entering: 7.1 ensuring formatting remains

7.   Edit cell C5 by entering: 5.1 ensuring formatting remains

8.   On Sheet 2, format the range of cells for retail price, namely C2:C7 for accounting

9.   On Sheet 2, edit cell C5 by entering: 5 ensuring formatting remains

10.   On Sheet 2, format cell C13 for currency in Yen with no decimal places

11.   Enter the amount of 145792.79 in cell C13 on sheet 2

12.   Save the file as a workbook with the file name as: **StockSale21** within the **TexAns** folder

13.   Close all open files

Exercise 22

Number and Fraction Formatting

1. Open the workbook file from the TexQuest folder named: **PayDay**

2. On the Product sheet, change the formatting for the range of cells C2:C14 to enable the contents of the cells to be shown as fractions to three digits

3. On the Wages sheet, alter the formatting for the range of cells B2:B7 to accommodate numbers with 7 decimal places

4. On the Wages sheet, format the range of cells C2:C7 to show fractions to two digits

5. Within the range of cells C2:C7 on the Wages sheet, enter into cell C2 the value 33.75, C3 enter 15.5, C4 enter 25.75 in cell C5 enter 35.25, in cell C6 enter 37.5 and into cell C7 enter 18.5

6. On the Wages sheet, format the range of cells D2:D7 to show numbers to two decimal places

7. On the Overtime sheet, format the range of cells B2:B4 for numbers to zero decimal places and to show thousand separators

8. On the Overtime sheet, in cell B2 enter: 1007450.97 and in cell B3 enter: 19372.01 and in cell B4 enter: 2948835

9. Save the file as a workbook with the file name as: **PayDay22** within the **TexAns** folder

10. Close all open files

Exercise 23

Text Formatting

1. Open the workbook file from the TexQuest folder named: **Vegetable**

2. In cell A1, format the text to use Garamond or Trebuchet or Verdana font

3. In cell A1, increase the size of the text to 20 point

4. In cells A3 and B3, increase the size of the text to 14 point

5. In cells A3 and B3, embolden the text and underline

6. In cell A14, italicise the text

7. In cell B6, change the font colour to red

8. In cells A4 and A10, change the background fill colour to yellow and the font colour to green

9. In cell B9, use strikethrough for the text to show the item has been cancelled

10. In cell A17, use superscript for the "th" of the text "5th revised version"

11. Save the file as a workbook with the file name as: **Vegetable23** within the **TexAns** folder

12. Close all open files

Exercise 24

Summary Formatting Section 1

1.   Open the workbook file from the TexQuest folder named: **soup**

2.   Increase the size of the text in cell A1 to 20 point

3.   Change the font colour for cell A3 to red

4.   Cells C8:C25 require formatting to show values as percentages

5.   In cell C8 enter the value: 2

6.   Throughout the range of cells C9:C25 show incremental input of values of 2 using series fill. Cell C9 should have the value of 4 and cell C10 should have the value of 6 and increments thereafter to continue to cell C25

7.   Throughout the range of cells D8:D25 input weekdays (Monday to Friday) and repeating for the duration of the range of cells, using series fill options

8.   In cell E11 enter the wording: Cancelled

9.   In cells A11:D11 strikethrough the text to show the item as cancelled

10. Embolden the contents of cell A12

11. In cell A23, edit the contents to now read: Onion Skin

12. In cell B30, increase the decimal place to 3 digits long

13. Save the file as a workbook with the file name as: **soup24** within the **TexAns** folder

14. Close all open files

Exercise 25

Summary Formatting Section 2

1. Open the workbook file from the TexQuest folder named: **staff**

2. In cell A1, increase the size of the text to 22 point

3. Range of cells A3:C3, decrease the size of the text to 12 point

4. Range of cells A3:C3, embolden the text

5. In cell A17, correct the text to read: Stock Control

6. In cell B4 enter the value: 72

7. In cell B11, input a formula calculating the difference of accounts staff cost between last year and this year

8. Edit cell C6 to now read: 19

9. Range of cells B16:C19 are required to be shown with US Dollars with no decimal place but using thousand separator

10. Using the cost for directors for this year and the amount of staff shown in cell B7, enter a formula in cell B22 calculating the cost per director

11. Embolden the contents of cells A18:C18

12. Cells A3:C3 and A15:C15 should have a yellow background fill

13. Save the file as a workbook with the file name as: **staff25** within the **TexAns** folder

14. Close all open files

Exercise 26

Clearing Formatting or Contents

1. Open the workbook file from the TexQuest folder named:
    Services

2. Delete the contents and formatting for cell G3

3. Delete the contents of cells: A3:B3

4. Remove the formatting only from the range A16:B19
    ensuring the contents remain

5. In cell G3 enter: Share Value

6. Save the file as a workbook with the file name as:
    Services26 within the **TexAns** folder

7. Close all open files

Exercise 27

Row Height and Column Width

1. Open the workbook file from the TexQuest folder named: **Merchant**

2. Adjust the width of column B to be precisely 235 pixels or 28.75 point

3. Increase the height of row 4 to ensure all the contents are visible

4. Adjust the width of column D to ensure all the contents within the column are visible

5. Adjust the height of row 10 to be sufficient for the contents within the row and not excessive, using autofit

6. Save the file as a workbook with the file name as: **Merchant27** within the **TexAns** folder

7. Close all open files

Exercise 28

Cell Alignment

1. Open the workbook file from the TexQuest folder named: **TownSales**

2. Cells C6:N10 require contents to be left aligned

3. Cells C5:N5 require contents to be centre aligned on the vertical and right aligned on the horizontal

4. Cell A6 needs the contents diagonally aligned counter clockwise

5. Cell B5 requires the contents diagonally aligned clockwise

6. Cell O5 needs the text shown vertically

7. In cell A1, centre the text across the table

8. Save the file as a workbook with the file name as: **TownSales28** within the **TexAns** folder

9. Close all open files

Exercise 29

Merge and Centre

1. Open the workbook file from the TexQuest folder named:
    Northern

2. The contents of cell A1 need to be merged across the range of cells A1:F1 and centred simultaneously

3. Cells B7 and C7 need merging and centred

4. In cell B7 which is now merged with cell C7 and centred, enter the text: Desktop

5. Cells D7 and E7 need merging and centred

6. In cell D7 which is now merged with cell E7, enter the text: Portable

7. Save the file as a workbook with the file name as: **Northern29** within the **TexAns** folder

8. Close all open files

Exercise 30

Text Wrapping

1. Open the workbook file from the TexQuest folder named:
    AddMember

2. Apply text wrapping to cell A1

3. The contents of cell A13 are not visible at the moment, use
    text wrapping but do not adjust column width

4. Apply text wrapping to cell A19

5. Save the file as a workbook with the file name as:
    AddMember30 within the **TexAns** folder

6. Close all open files

Exercise 31

Shrink to Fit

1. Open the workbook file from the TexQuest folder named: **MemberForm**

2. The contents within Cell A1 are too large for the size of the cell. Shrink the text to fit the size of the cell without adjusting height or width

3. Shrink to fit the contents of cell A15

4. Cells B4:B7 require the contents to fit the current width of column B, apply shrink to fit to this range of cells

5. Cell A18 needs the contents to fit the current size of cell, apply shrink to fit to this cell

6. Save the file as a workbook with the file name as: **MemberForm31** within the **TexAns** folder

7. Close all open files

Exercise 32

Borders

1. Open the workbook file from the TexQuest folder named: **drums**

2. Range of cells B6:D9 require a red coloured thick box around the outside

3. The total after discount is the sales price in cell E29, place a double lined border at the bottom and a one line border at the top of the cell

4. Cells A16:E22 need a border outside and inside for every cell within the range

5. A border surrounding the whole of the invoice data is required, from cell A1 down to cell E35. Use the colour green for this border

6. Save the file as a workbook with the file name as: **drums32** within the **TexAns** folder

7. Close all open files

Exercise 33

Alignment, wrapping, effects summary

1. Open the workbook file from the TexQuest folder named: **employees**

2. Merge cells A10:A15

3. In cell A10, enter the text: Count

4. In cell A10, rotate text upward

5. Cell B1 requires the contents centred vertically and horizontally

6. Shrink the contents of cell A1 to fit the size of the cell without adjusting the row height or column width

7. Cell C9 needs the text to wrap to show all text correctly, without reducing the font size

8. Cells A18:A23 require merging

9. In cell A18, enter the text: Estimate

10. Angle the text in cell A18 to counter clockwise direction

11. Place a red border around the outside of cells A18:C23

12. Increase the width of Column C to accommodate all of the entries within cells

13. Place a double line black border around cells B4:C6

14. Left align contents within cells C10:C23

15. Save the file as a workbook with the file name as: **employees33** within the **TexAns** folder

16. Close all open files

Exercise 34

Format rows and columns

1. Open the workbook file from the TexQuest folder named: **account**

2. All contents of column A must be left aligned

3. In cell A4, enter: Deposit

4. Format column B for long form date (eg. 31 March 2009)

5. Format column C for accounting style in Euro currency

6. Enter the following data into the relevant cells: B1 enter: 12/3/2010, B2 enter: 1/3/2011, B3 enter: 31/04/2011, B4 enter: 1-5-2011

7. Enter the following data into the relevant cells: C1 enter: 1250 , C2 enter: 5400, C3 enter: 3440, C4 enter: 450

8. Embolden contents within all cells within row 3

9. In cell AA3, enter: Not for use

10. Save the file as a workbook with the file name as: **account34** within the **TexAns** folder

11. Close all open files

Exercise 35

Insert, Delete and Move rows and columns

1. Open the workbook file from the TexQuest folder named: **teachers**

2. Insert a column between columns B and C

3. In cell C2, enter the text: Gender

4. Cells C3:C178 require filling with the text: Male

5. Cells C179:266 require filling with the text: Female

6. Delete column E as all the data is the same and is not needed any further

7. Move column D to be the last column

8. Delete any empty columns remaining after the move

9. Insert a blank row between rows 1 and 2

10. Locate the record for the name of Primo Boffa and delete the whole record (ie. Delete the entire row)

11. Save the file as a workbook with the file name as: **teachers35** within the **TexAns** folder

12. Close all open files

Exercise 36

Hiding and Revealing Columns and Rows

1. Open the workbook file from the TexQuest folder named: **purchase**

2. Reveal the hidden column C

3. Hide columns H and J

4. Hide row 8 for the Paisley record

5. Reveal rows 11 and 12

6. Print 1 copy of the worksheet

7. Save the file as a workbook with the file name as: **purchase36** within the **TexAns** folder

8. Close all open files

Exercise 37

Freeze Panes

1. Open the workbook file from the TexQuest folder named: **sturesults**

2. Freeze the appropriate column to ensure the student name is static when scrolling to the right

3. Scroll to the right until the Overall Total values within column S are shown immediately next to the student names

4. Save the file as a workbook with the file name as: **sturesults37** within the **TexAns** folder

5. Close all open files

6. Open the workbook file from the TexQuest folder named: **teachers**

7. Freeze the appropriate row to ensure the headings for each column (ie. First, Surname, Date Engaged, Paid, Ranking, Based) are viewable when scrolling down the page

8. Scroll down to show the last record immediately under the headings

9. Save the file as a workbook with the file name as: **teachers37** within the **TexAns** folder

10. Close all open files

Exercise 38

Row and Column Control Summary

1. Open the workbook file from the TexQuest folder named: **dues**

2. Delete rows 1 through to 5 to enable the heading row to occupy the top row

3. Hide Column C

4. Move column B being First Name to before the column headed: Surname

5. Freeze the appropriate header row to enable the headings to be viewed when scrolling down the page

6. Scroll down to the last record, namely: Andrew Watt, ensuring this record is the only one in view immediately after the headings

7. Save the file as a workbook with the file name as: **dues38** within the **TexAns** folder

8. Close all open files

Exercise 39

Formatting and Control Summary

1. Open the workbook file from the TexQuest folder named: **secondhalf**

2. Embolden and double underline the contents of cell A1

3. Change the font colour for cells B6:B9 to the colour white

4. Fit the contents of cell B10 to the current cell size using shrink to fit and without adjusting column width or row height

5. Hide columns C through to H

6. Delete column O

7. Hide row 7, being the record for South

8. Make the text in cell A6 vertical

9. Use shrink to fit for the text in cell A6

10. Centre vertically and horizontally all text within cells I5:N5

11. Apply a comma thousand separator for cells I6:N10

12. Content in B5 needs angled counter clockwise

13. Save the file as a workbook with the file name as: **secondhalf39** within the **TexAns** folder

14. Close all open files

Exercise 40

Sheet insertion and deletion

1. Open the workbook file from the TexQuest folder named: **process**

2. Delete sheet named: blank

3. Insert a new sheet after the sheet named: meetings

4. Delete sheet named: payment

5. Insert a new sheet at the end of all current sheets

6. Save the file as a workbook with the file name as: **process40** within the **TexAns** folder

7. Close all open files

Exercise 41

Sheet renaming, copying and moving

1. Open the workbook file from the TexQuest folder named: **controlsheet**

2. Move Sheet 1 in between Legends and Sheet 2

3. Duplicate sheet named: process

4. Rename Sheet 4 to: notes

5. Open the workbook file from the TexQuest folder named: sheethere

6. Copy the emergency sheet from the controlsheet workbook in between Sheet 1 and 2 of the workbook file named: sheethere

7. Save the sheethere file as a workbook with the file name as: **sheethere41** within the **TexAns** folder

8. Close the workbook named: sheethere

9. Return to the workbook named: controlsheet

10. Insert a new sheet at the end of all others and name the new sheet: cover

11. Save the file as a workbook with the file name as: **controlsheet41** within the **TexAns** folder

12. Close all open files

Exercise 42

Colour sheet tabs

1. Open the workbook file from the TexQuest folder named: **bestmonth**

2. Apply the colour yellow to the sheet tabs for August, September and October

3. Apply the colour red to the sheet named: November

4. Save the file as a workbook with the file name as: **bestmonth42** within the **TexAns** folder

5. Close all open files

Exercise 43

Sheet Control Summary

1. Open the workbook file from the TexQuest folder named: **feechange**

2. Open the workbook file from the TexQuest folder named: **feecost**

3. Copy the cost worksheet from within the feechange workbook in between Sheet1 and Sheet2 of the feecost workbook

4. Save the feecost file as a workbook with the file name as: **feecost43** within the **TexAns** folder

5. Close the feecost43 workbook but keep the feechange workbook open

6. Return to the workbook named: feechange and delete the sheets named: old and ancient

7. Rename Sheet4 to: list

8. Apply a green colour to the sheets named: 2009 and 2010

9. Move the 2011 sheet to be found immediately after the 2010 sheet

10. Save the file as a workbook with the file name as: **feechange43** within the **TexAns** folder

11. Close all open files

Exercise 44

Copy and Paste Formatting

1. Open the workbook file from the TexQuest folder named: **Jammy**

2. Copy the formatting for cell A9 to cell A7 without altering the contents of the cells

3. Copy the formatting from cell E6 to cell E8 without altering the contents of the cells

4. Using the fill handle, copy the formatting only, across from cell A4 through the range of cells B4:F4 without altering the contents of the cells

5. Using the fill handle, copy the formatting only, down from cells A16:B16 through cells A17:B18

6. Copy the formatting from cell B2 of Sheet2 of the same workbook into cell F13 of Sheet1

7. Save the file as a workbook with the file name as: **Jammy44** within the **TexAns** folder

8. Close all open files

Exercise 45

Format Painter

1. Open the workbook file from the TexQuest folder named:
    frev

2. Using format painter for one instance, copy the formatting
    of cell C5 into cell D5

3. Using format painter multiple instances, copy the
    formatting of cell B22 and apply to the following cells: B7,
    B11, B14

4. Using format painter multiple instances, copy the
    formatting of cell C22 and apply to the following cells: C14,
    C15, C16

5. Using the format painter multiple instances, copy the
    formatting of cell D22 and apply to the following cells: D7,
    D9, D11, D14, D15

6. Save the file as a workbook with the file name as: **frev45**
    within the **TexAns** folder

7. Close all open files

Exercise 46

Conditional Formatting

1. Open the workbook file from the TexQuest folder named: **frev_v2**

2. Using conditional formatting, arrange for any cells in the range of cells B6:B17 having a value greater than shown in cell B22 to be highlighted with light red fill and dark red text

3. Using conditional formatting, arrange for any cells in the range of cells: C6:C17 having a value greater than shown in cell C22 to be highlighted with yellow fill and dark yellow text

4. Using conditional formatting, arrange for any cells in the range of cells: D6:D17 having a value greater than shown in cell D22 to be highlighted with green fill and dark green text

5. Change the value in cell: B8 to now read: 995.00 and ensure the conditional formatting is working correctly

6. Change the value in cell: D7 to now read: 4400.00 and ensure the conditional formatting is working correctly in this column as well

7. Save the file as a workbook with the file name as: **frev_v2_46** within the **TexAns** folder

8. Close all open files

Exercise 47

Autosum

1. Open the workbook file from the TexQuest folder named: **maternity**

2. Within the female tab sheet, in cell B18, using autosum, insert a formula for calculating the total of female babies delivered for the year

3. Within the male tab sheet, in cell B18, using autosum, insert a formula for calculating the total of male babies delivered for the year

4. Within the bottles tab sheet, in cell B12, using autosum, insert a formula for calculating the total of cell range: B8:B11 (do not incorporate cell B7 into the calculation)

5. Within the bottles tab sheet, in cell B17, using autosum, calculate the total unused bottles

6. Save the file as a workbook with the file name as: **maternity47** within the **TexAns** folder

7. Close all open files

Exercise 48

Basic Functions

1. Open the workbook file from the TexQuest folder named: **rating**

2. In cell E24, enter a formula with function enabling the counting of amount of customers

3. In cell H24, enter a formula with function enabling the counting of customers with children

4. Save the file as a workbook with the file name as: **rating48** within the **TexAns** folder

5. Close all open files

Exercise 49

Lowest, Highest and average

1. Open the workbook file from the TexQuest folder named: **age**

2. In cell B17 of the age sheet, enter a formula with relevant function to calculate the youngest age within the list of employees

3. Edit cell B12 to read: 16

4. In cell B18 of the age sheet, enter a formula with relevant function to calculate the highest age within the list of employees

5. Edit cell B13 to now read: 62

6. In cell B19 of the age sheet, enter a formula with relevant function to calculate the average age of all employees within the list

7. Select the wages sheet tab of the workbook. In cell B9 of the wages sheet, enter a formula with relevant function to calculate the average salary across the whole salary structure

8. Save the file as a workbook with the file name as: **age49** within the **TexAns** folder

9. Close all open files

Exercise 50

Intermediate Function Summary 1

1. Open the workbook file from the TexQuest folder named: **Results**

2. Using column H. Within cell H29, enter a formula with relevant function to calculate the count of students

3. In cell H30, enter a formula with relevant function to calculate the average result from the grand totals

4. In cell H31, enter a formula with relevant function to calculate the highest result from the grand totals

5. In cell H32, enter a formula with relevant function to calculate the lowest result from the grand totals

6. Edit cell G23 now to read: 35

7. Edit cell E26 now to read: 7

8. Save the file as a workbook with the file name as: **Results50** within the **TexAns** folder

9. Close all open files

Exercise 51

Copy and Paste Formulae and edit

1.   Open the workbook file from the TexQuest folder named: **season**

2.   In cell B11, enter a formula to calculate the difference between the value for the years 2009 and 2014 only, plus a seasonal adjustment value as shown in cell B25

3.   Copy the formula from cell B11 and paste into cell B21

4.   Edit, if required, the formula within cell B21 to consider the requirement to calculate the difference between the years 2009   and   2025,   with   the   seasonal   adjustment compensation value incorporated as required

5.   Edit cell B25, for the seasonal adjustment compensation value to now read: 750

6.   Save the file as a workbook with the file name as: **season51** within the **TexAns** folder

7.   Close all open files

Exercise 52

Relative Referencing

1.   Open the workbook file from the TexQuest folder named: **bakers**

2.   In cell B18, enter a formula to calculate the total for Rolls

3.   Replicate the formula from cell B18 to cell C18 relevant to the total for Bread and continue over to cell D18 to calculate the total for Cakes

4.   Once again, replicate the formula from cell D18 over into cell E18 to provide the grand total for all products

5.   In cell A20, enter the text: Average Summer Cakes

6.   In cell B20, enter a formula with relevant function to calculate the average value for cakes during June, July and August

7.   In cell B21, enter an appropriate formula to show the value of cakes for the month of June

8.   Replicate the entry within cell B21, down to cells B22 and B23 to show the cakes value for the months of July and August respectively

9.   Save the file as a workbook with the file name as: **bakers52** within the **TexAns** folder

10.   Close all open files

Exercise 53

More Relative Referencing

1. Open the workbook file from the TexQuest folder named: **magazook**

2. In cell E14, enter a formula to calculate the total price, considering the unit price and quantity

3. Replicate the formula from cell E14 down into cells E15, E16, E17 for each relevant service

4. Save the file as a workbook with the file name as: **magazook43** within the **TexAns** folder

5. Close all open files

Exercise 54

Intermediate Functions Summary 2

1. Open the workbook file from the TexQuest folder named: **dragons**

2. In cell E8, enter a formula with relevant function to calculate the total attendance for the 1st Quarter

3. Replicate the formula from cell E8 downward through to cell E11 for the calculation of attendance for each quarter

4. In cell B12, enter a formula with relevant function to calculate the sub total for the 1st team

5. Replicate the formula from cell B12 across through cells C12, D12, E12

6. In cell B13, enter a formula with relevant function to calculate the average attendance for the 1st team

7. Replicate the formula from cell B13 across through cells C13, D13, E13

8. In cell B14, enter a formula with relevant function to calculate the largest attendance for the 1st team

9. Replicate the formula from cell B14 across through cells C14, D14, E14

10. Save the file as a workbook with the file name as: **dragons54** within the **TexAns** folder

11. Close all open files

Exercise 55

Absolute Referencing

1. Open the workbook file from the TexQuest folder named: **commission**

2. In cell G5, enter a formula to calculate the amount of commission relative to the total income, using the commission rate detailed in cell B21. Absolute referencing should be applied where appropriate.

3. Replicate the formula down through the cells from G5 to cell G16

4. Commencing in cell H5, enter a formula to calculate the share of commission based upon the split per month noted in cell B24

5. Replicate the formula from cell H5 through to cell H16 applying absolute referencing where appropriate

6. Save the file as a workbook with the file name as: **commission55** within the **TexAns** folder

7. Close all open files

Exercise 56

Calculating Tax using Absolute Referencing

1. Open the workbook file from the TexQuest folder named: **cameras**

2. Select the sheet tab named: caw

3. In cell F18, enter a formula to calculate the amount of tax upon the net total using the rate of tax shown in cell C25

4. Replicate the formula from cell F18 down through all the cells to F22, ensuring absolute referencing is employed where appropriate

5. Select the sheet tab named: tax

6. In cell B13 if the tax sheet, enter a formula to calculate the amount of tax payable based upon the tax rate mentioned in cell H6 and upon the income shown in cell B12

7. Replicate the formula across all the cells from cell B13 through to cell G13

8. Save the file as a workbook with the file name as: **cameras56** within the **TexAns** folder

9. Close all open files

Exercise 57

Relative and Absolute referencing summary 1

1. Open the workbook file from the TexQuest folder named:
    packet

2. In cell C4, enter a formula to calculate the wage taking into
    consideration the hourly rate and the hours per week as
    shown in cell B13

3. Replicate the formula down from cell C4 through to C11,
    applying absolute referencing where applicable

4. In cell D4, enter a formula to calculate the tax payable
    upon the actual wage from cell C4 and the rate of tax
    shown in cell B15

5. Replicate the formula down from cell D4 through to D11,
    applying absolute referencing where applicable

6. In cell E4, enter a simple formula to calculate the pay
    packet value from the wage in cell C4 less the calculated
    tax shown in cell D4

7. Replicate the calculation down from cell E4 through to E11

8. Save the file as a workbook with the file name as:
    packet57 within the **TexAns** folder

9. Close all open files

Exercise 58

Relative and Absolute Referencing Summary 2

1. Open the workbook file from the TexQuest folder named: **donation**

2. In cell F4, enter a formula to calculate the donation amount based upon the donation rate shown in cell E26 and the earnings for the first record

3. Replicate the formula from cell F4 down through to F22, using relative and absolute referencing where required

4. In cell F23, enter a formula using a function to total all the donation values

5. In cell B30, enter a formula to calculate the share of donations for the Northern area considering the total donation and the equal split rate in cell E32

6. Copy the formula in cell B30 across through cells: C30, D30, E30 using relative and absolute referencing where applicable

7. Save the file as a workbook with the file name as: **donation58** within the **TexAns** folder

8. Close all open files

Exercise 59

Statistical functions

1.　Open the workbook file from the TexQuest folder named: **cables**

2.　Taking into consideration all other months in the year figures related to cables despatched and amount of cables requiring re-work, enter a formula with relevant function in cell M9 to forecast the amount of cables possibly requiring re-work for the month of December

3.　In cell B15, enter a formula with relevant function to show the rank of December among all other months of the year, in relation to quantities of cable despatched

4.　Save the file as a workbook with the file name as: **cables59** within the **TexAns** folder

5.　Close all open files

Exercise 60

Date and Time functions

1. Open the workbook file from the TexQuest folder named: **timed**

2. In cell F4, enter a formula with relevant function to calculate the amount of days taken in transit, noting the date of despatch, arrival date and considering holidays shown in the range of cells: B11:B13

3. Replicate the formula from cell F4 down through every cell and including cell: F7

4. In cell B17, enter a formula with relevant function to display the current date. The formula must always show the current date for the date to which the file is opened

5. In cell B18, enter a formula with relevant function to display the current date / time, whereby the time will update in the same manner as the current date every time the file is opened

6. Save the file as a workbook with the file name as: **timed60** within the **TexAns** folder

7. Close all open files

Exercise 61

Look up functions

1. Open the workbook file from the TexQuest folder named: **Routes**

2. Within the Routes workbook, navigate to the sheet named: Invoice

3. In cell B14, enter a formula with relevant function for the insertion of the route relevant to the code within cell: A14 from the table located on the sheet tab named: Transport

4. Replicate the formula from within cell B14 on the Invoice sheet, down through and including cell B18, ensuring correct referencing throughout

5. Remaining within the Invoice sheet, in cell D14, enter a formula with relevant function for the insertion of the selling price based upon the code within cell: A14 from the table located on the sheet tab named: Transport

6. Similarly, replicate the formula from within cell D14 on the Invoice sheet, down through and including cell D18, ensuring correct referencing throughout

7. Save the file as a workbook with the file name as: **Routes61** within the **TexAns** folder

8. Close all open files

Exercise 62

Financial functions

1. Open the workbook file from the TexQuest folder named:
    shares

2. In cell B9 of the futures sheet of the shares workbook,
    enter a formula with relevant function to calculate the
    future value of the investment based upon the information
    provided within the sheet

3. Navigate to the loan worksheet within the same workbook

4. In cell B9 of the loan sheet, enter a formula with relevant
    function to calculate the monthly payments for the loan
    based upon the data located within the loan sheet

5. Edit cell B7 to now read: 17500

6. Save the file as a workbook with the file name as:
    shares62 within the **TexAns** folder

7. Close all open files

Exercise 63

Database functions

1. Open the workbook file from the TexQuest folder named: **areacars**

2. In cell G4, enter a formula with relevant function to calculate the highest recorded sale for the Inverclyde area listed within the table . Use cells G1 and G2 to contain the criteria for fulfilment of function

3. In cell I4, enter a formula with relevant function to calculate the total car sale value for the Aberdeen area gathering the total from the table data. Use cells I1 and I2 to contain the criteria

4. In cell K4, enter a formula with relevant function to calculate the total car sale value for the Glasgow area gathering the total from the table data. Using cells K1, K2 for specific criteria

5. In cell M4, enter a formula with relevant function to calculate the average amount of cars sold on the 24/8/09, gathering the data from the table supplied. Use cells M1 and M2 to contain the criteria

6. Save the file as a workbook with the file name as: **areacars63** within the **TexAns** folder

7. Close all open files

Exercise 64

Logical functions

1. Open the workbook file from the TexQuest folder named: **BDM**

2. In cell G6, enter a formula to calculate the percentage of overall sales mentioned in cell E18

3. In cell G7, enter a formula to calculate the percentage of overall sales mentioned in cell E18, similar to the formula entered in cell G6. Continue to replicate the formula through all cells down to cell G17

4. In cell H6, enter a formula with relevant function to calculate whether the total sales for this record of January is lesser than or equal to the target total shown in cell B22. If the total sales meets this criteria then cell H6 must declare the text: "Below Target", and if the total sales for the record is above the target then H6 should declare the text: "Good Total"

5. Replicate the formula in H6 through to cell: H17

6. In cell I6, enter a formula with relevant function to calculate whether the total sales for the record is above target, in which case the commission should be calculated on the total sales amount based upon the percentage shown in cell B26, if below target then the commission rate shown in cell B27 must be used within the calculation

7. Replicate the formula in cell I6 through to cell: I17

8. Save the file as a workbook with the file name as: **BDM64** within the **TexAns** folder

9. Close all open files

Exercise 65

Text functions

1. Open the workbook file from the TexQuest folder named: **it_usernames**

2. In cell G2, enter a formula with relevant function to calculate a username consisting of First Name, Surname and Age. Do not place spaces in between each fields used within the construction of username

3. Continue the entering of the formula with relevant function to calculate usernames for every record down the list to cell: G61

4. In cell I2, enter a formula with relevant function to calculate the total amount of characters in the username from cell G2

5. Replicate the formula from I2 down through every cell to the bottom of the list, being cell: I61

6. In cell K2, enter a formula with relevant function to show the city name from cell D2 without the 4 digit area code

7. Replicate the formula from K2 down through every cell to the bottom of the list

8. Save the file as a workbook with the file name as: **it_usernames65** within the **TexAns** folder

9. Close all open files

Exercise 66

Inserting Web Hyperlinks

1. Open the workbook file from the TexQuest folder named: **sportsorg**

2. Navigate to the worksheet within the sportsorg workbook named: web

3. In cell B8, insert a hyperlink to the website of the Olympic Movement with the address: http://www.olympic.org

4. In cell B9, insert at hyperlink to the website of the Scottish Football Associate at: http://www.scottishfa.co.uk

5. In cell A16, insert a hyperlink to the website of the NFL USA at: http://www.nfl.com with only the wording shown in cell A16 as: This is a link to the NFL website

6. Navigate to the worksheet within the sportsorg workbook named: mail

7. In cell B8, insert a hyperlink to the e-mail address for the SFA: info@scottishfa.co.uk offering the subject line as: My interest in the beautiful game in Scotland

8. In cell A15, insert a hyperlink to the e-mail address of the Olympic Movement: pressoffice@olympic.org but only display the text for the link as: Olympic Movement Mail

9. Save the file as a workbook with the file name as: **sportsorg66** within the **TexAns** folder

10. Close all open files

Exercise 67

More Hyperlinks

1. Open the workbook file from the TexQuest folder named: **links**

2. In cell B3, insert a hyperlink to the Microsoft website at: http://www.microsoft.com

3. In cell B4, insert a hyperlink to a Pro-Photographer website at http://www.professional-photographer.eu

4. In cell A10, insert a hyperlink using display text "Link to the CIA website" and link to http://www.cia.gov

5. In cell A13, insert a hyperlink using display text "SightSavers E-mail link is here" and link to the e-mail address for SightSavers: info@sightsavers.org offering the subject line as: Wishing to donate soon

6. In cell A15, using the current contents of the cell, insert a hyperlink to the sportsorg workbook file located within the TexQuest folder

7. Add a screen tip to the hyperlink in cell A15, meaning if a user moves over the cell with their pointer, the following text would appear as assistance: Click this link to be taken to the sportsorg workbook file

8. Save the file as a workbook with the file name as: **links67** within the **TexAns** folder

9. Close all open files

Exercise 68

Editing Hyperlinks

1.   Open the workbook file from the TexQuest folder named: **schedule**

2.   Edit the hyperlink in cell C5 to display text: Glasgow City Council website

3.   Further edit the hyperlink in cell C5, changing the web address to: http://www.glasgow.gov.uk/en/Visitors and edit the screen tip to now read: Click here for the visitors section of the Glasgow City Council website

4.   Edit the hyperlink in cell C7 to display text: Information for Australian government

5.   Further edit the hyperlink in cell C7, changing the web address to: http://www.australia.gov.au and provide a screen tip reading: This link takes you to the Australian government website

6.   Edit the hyperlink in cell A11 to provide a screen tip reading: Direct mailing to Scotland Org

7.   Further edit the hyperlink in cell A11 by changing the e-mail address to: info@scotland.org

8.   Save the file as a workbook with the file name as: **schedule68** within the **TexAns** folder

9.   Close all open files

Exercise 69

Skills assessment 1

1. Open the workbook file from the TexQuest folder named: **travel**

2. Increase the size of the font in cell A1 to 20 point

3. Apply a yellow background colour to cells B6:D9

4. Place a blue border around the outside of cells B6:B9

5. In cell C12, enter a formula with relevant function to display the current date. Whenever the file is opened the system date to which the file is opened is applied

6. In cell E27, insert a formula with relevant function to calculate the total of all the net totals

7. In cell E28, insert a formula with relevant function to calculate the discount rate based upon the code shown in cell B28 relating to the table shown in range: C38:D41

8. In cell E29, insert a formula to calculate the total less the discount value, providing a final amount

9. In cell E33, insert a formula with relevant function to calculate the current date plus 30 days to provide a due date for payment

10. In cell B21, insert a hyperlink to http://www.gov.sg leaving the current text, incorporating screen tip: Link to Singov

11. Save the file as a workbook with the file name as: **travel69** within the **TexAns** folder

12. Close all open files

Exercise 70

Inserting Comments

1.   Open the workbook file from the TexQuest folder named: **fakts**

2.   In cell B14, insert a comment reading: Possibly reduced to 4 days with an extra day compiling information related to individual requirements

3.   In cell E6, insert a comment reading: CEO of parent company

4.   In cell D17, insert a comment reading: Total allocation for this course could exceed 250 delegates with subsidiary companies providing even greater demand within 12 months

5.   In cell F22, insert a comment reading: This amount does not include any discounts available

6.   Save the file as a workbook with the file name as: **fakts70** within the **TexAns** folder

7.   Close all open files

Exercise 71

Editing Comments

1. Open the workbook file from the TexQuest folder named: **cpd**

2. In cell B15, edit the comment to now read: Due to get married in August with surname changing to McMaster

3. In cell F19, edit the comment to now read: Management activities incomplete due to illness for past 3 months

4. In cell F26, edit the comment to now read: Additional Management activities requested by the employee and verified as being appropriate by departmental head in conjunction with director of HR

5. Delete the comment associated with cell B8

6. Delete the comment associated with cell D17

7. Hide the comment for cell G10

8. Save the file as a workbook with the file name as: **cpd71** within the **TexAns** folder

9. Close all open files

Exercise 72

Find and Replace

1. Open the workbook file from the TexQuest folder named: **jackets**

2. Find all instances of the place name Hamilton and replace with the place name Coatbridge. Ensure the surname of Shamilton is not altered

3. Find all instances of the place name Springboig and replace with the place name Springburn

4. Locate all characters with the colour of red font and change to centre align, bold and italic

5. Find all instances of the brand Marke and replace with the brand name TamMan

6. Locate all instances of the word "Sunday" and replace with "All"

7. Locate all instances of the word "Saturday" and replace with "Restricted"

8. Save the file as a workbook with the file name as: **jackets72** within the **TexAns** folder

9. Close all open files

Exercise 73

Inserting Pictures and ClipArt

1. Open the workbook file from the TexQuest folder named: **review**

2. With cell D11 being the top left hand corner, place the image file located within the TexQuest folder named: fitba

3. With cell G11 as the insertion point, search clipart for an image of a soccer ball and insert

4. Save the file as a workbook with the file name as: **review73** within the **TexAns** folder

5. Close all open files

Exercise 74

Object sizing and positioning

1. Open the workbook file from the TexQuest folder named: **victors**

2. Resize the image of aeroplane and sun to height of 4 cm and width of 5 cm

3. Position the image of aeroplane and sun neatly between cells C4 and C12

4. Resize the water and hills photograph on the right hand side of the header, to have an image size of precisely 5.5 cm in height and 17.7 cm in width

5. Position the photograph directly under the table with the top line of the image being around row 22

6. Crop the photograph from the bottom by 1.2 cm

7. Edit the alternative display text to read: Panoramic view of Wemyss Bay in Scotland

8. Save the file as a workbook with the file name as: **victors74** within the **TexAns** folder

9. Close all open files

Exercise 75

Hyper linking Objects

1. Open the workbook file from the TexQuest folder named: **users**

2. Select cell C5

3. Insert the photograph file located within the TexQuest folder named: cornalees

4. Add a hyperlink association with the photograph to enable a user to click on the image and be taken to the following web address: http://www.Texazine.com

5. Provide a screen tip reading: Clicking on this photograph of The Cornalees in Greenock will take you to the Texazine website

6. Add a hyperlink association to the rectangle above the table reading "Magazook Link", enabling a user to click on the rectangle and their web browser to open at the following web address: http://www.Magazook.com

7. Provide a screen tip for the rectangle reading the following: Clicking here provides a link to the Magazook website with links to Texazine plus much more

8. Save the file as a workbook with the file name as: **users75** within the **TexAns** folder

9. Close all open files

Exercise 76

Inserting Shapes

1. Open the workbook file from the TexQuest folder named: **fish**

2. In cell F16, place a large left arrow from the block arrows category of shapes, pointing to cell E16

3. Cell E20 requires highlighting by placing an oval from the basic shapes category of shapes around the cell. Ensure the contents of the cell remain in full view

4. To show acceptability, cell B24 requires a smiley face placed to the right of the cell

5. Cell B26 requires an oval from the basic shapes category of shapes placed around the cell. Ensure the contents of the cell remain in full view

6. Save the file as a workbook with the file name as: **fish76** within the **TexAns** folder

7. Close all open files

Exercise 77

Inserting a Text Box, WordArt and Symbol

1. Open the workbook file from the TexQuest folder named: **PCInvoice**

2. Within the area to the left of the name "Bitz N PCs Supplier of Computer Parts" place some WordArt, using any design of your choice but applying blue colour to the lettering. The wording needs to be: Bitz N PCs

3. Size the WordArt to occupy the bulk of the area around the range of cells: A1:B10

4. The copyright notice in cell A27 requires the copyright symbol placed somewhere next to the cell, example: ©

5. To confirm the verification of the invoice item, place a tick or check mark within cell F18, example: √

6. Cells F19:F21 also require a tick or check mark inserted, example: √

7. Place a text box anywhere upon the invoice sheet and type the following text inside: This Invoice is a sample only and is not valid

8. Increase the font size of the text box to 18 point

9. Move the text box to approximately the middle of the table within the invoice sheet

10. Rotate the text box to 328 degrees

11. Save the file as a workbook with the file name as: **PCInvoice77** within the **TexAns** folder

12. Close all open files

Exercise 78

Editing and Deleting Objects

1. Open the workbook file from the TexQuest folder named: **brawteach**

2. Delete the image on the left hand side of the two images

3. Group the remaining image of the green pointing teacher with the WordArt consisting of the words: Class Teaching

4. Move the remaining image of the green pointing teacher with the WordArt to a more central position under the wording at the top of the sheet

5. Edit the image. Change the colour of green teacher image to become red

6. Apply a red intense effect accent 2 style to the whole of the teacher image

7. Copy the image of the teacher and place a copy underneath the listings, at about row 275

8. Save the file as a workbook with the file name as: **brawteach78** within the **TexAns** folder

9. Close all open files

Exercise 79

Inserting Sound Files

1. Open the workbook file from the TexQuest folder named: **accent**

2. In cell G12, display as an icon, insert the sound file located within the TexQuest folder named: dinnaeken

3. Resize and move the sound file icon within cell G12 to within the boundaries of the said cell

4. In cell G15, display as an icon, insert the sound file located within the TexQuest folder named: dram

5. Resize and move the sound file icon within cell G15 to within the boundaries of the said cell

6. In cell G18, display as an icon, insert the sound file located within the TexQuest folder named: lum

7. Resize and move the sound file icon within cell G18 to within the boundaries of the said cell

8. Test each of the sound files to ensure embedded correctly. Each file is Windows Media Audio format and requires appropriate software to review

9. Save the file as a workbook with the file name as: **accent79** within the **TexAns** folder

10. Close all open files

Exercise 80

Using the Spell Checker and Thesaurus

1. Open the workbook file from the TexQuest folder named: **Accounts4u**

2. Invoke the spellchecker for the whole of the spreadsheet, altering words where appropriate to correct the various spelling errors

3. In cell D12, use the thesaurus within Microsoft Office Excel to change the word "remaining" to the second of the list returned within the thesaurus

4. Save the file as a workbook with the file name as: **Accounts4u80** within the **TexAns** folder

5. Close all open files

Exercise 81

Using the Research Tool

1. Open the workbook file from the TexQuest folder named:
    research

2. There are many reasons for using the Research Tool provided within Microsoft Office. Column A of the sheet indicates a reason for requiring research. Column B of the sheet contains words or phrases to be researched. Column C, within relevant cells, provide a line of information retrieved from the Research Tool

3. Cells B14 and B15 require translation into Spanish, the reason provided within cells A14 and A15 respectively. Using the Translation Tool, insert the translation into cells C14 and C15 respectively

4. Save the file as a workbook with the file name as: **research81** within the **TexAns** folder

5. Close all open files

Exercise 82

Sorting Lists

1. Open the workbook file from the TexQuest folder named: **magazines**

2. Within the worksheet named title, sort the list into Alphabetical Ascending order of Magazine Title

3. Within the worksheet named price, sort the list into lowest price ascending to highest and secondly sorting by Magazine Title on a lower level

4. Within the worksheet named category, sort the list using levels, firstly by descending Category, secondly by ascending Price, thirdly by ascending Magazine Title

5. Within the worksheet named horiz, sort the horizontal list of Magazines in A to Z order. It is not necessary to adjust column widths after sorting

6. Save the file as a workbook with the file name as: **magazines82** within the **TexAns** folder

7. Close all open files

Exercise 83

Filtering Lists

1. Open the workbook file from the TexQuest folder named: **club**

2. Filter the list to show all Male members who have not paid

3. Copy the data of all males who have not paid into the MalesOwing sheet of the workbook, pasting into cell A1

4. Clear the previous filtering

5. Filter the list to show all Female members who have paid

6. Copy the data of all female members who have paid, into the FemalesPaid sheet of the workbook, commencing at cell A1

7. Clear the previous filtering

8. Filter the list to show all members from the postcode and town of 1200 Portville who have paid

9. Copy the data of all members from 1200 Portville who have paid, into the PortvillePaid sheet of the workbook, commencing at cell A1

10. Clear the previous filtering

11. Filter the list to show all members with the first name of either Lisa or Elaine or Heather

12. Save the file as a workbook with the file name as: **club83** within the **TexAns** folder

13. Close all open files

Exercise 84

More Filtering of Lists

1. Open the workbook file from the TexQuest folder named: **motorsale**

2. Filter the list to show only sales by the Manager of Reilly, with sales in the Area of Inverclyde only

3. Copy the data and paste into the worksheet named Reilly commencing at cell: A1

4. Clear the previous filter

5. Filter the list to show only sales from the Area of Aberdeen that have been Confirmed as Yes

6. Copy the data and paste into the worksheet named Aberdeen

7. Clear the previous filter

8. Filter the list to show only sales from the month of September that have been Confirmed as Yes

9. Copy the data and paste into the worksheet named September

10. Remove all filters from the motors sheet

11. Save the file as a workbook with the file name as: **motorsale84** within the **TexAns** folder

12. Close all open files

Exercise 85

Advanced Filtering

1. Open the workbook file from the TexQuest folder named: **packs**

2. Filter the list to show only records for between and including the dates of: 28/2/09 and 5/3/09

3. Copy the data and paste into the worksheet named begmarch

4. Clear the previous filter

5. Filter the list to show only records whereby the Team name does not end with a 'y' or 'n' and whereby the quantity of packs are within the top 10 percent

6. Copy the data and paste into the worksheet named top10yn

7. Clear the previous filter

8. Filter the list to show only records whereby the quantity of packs is less than 100 and more than or equal to 150, also where the Team name begins with 'O' or ends with 'y', also where the date is in the second quarter, as well as filtering down to only records with the Town as Leixlip

9. Copy the data and paste into the worksheet named Leixlip

10. Remove all filters

11. Save the file as a workbook with the file name as: **packs85** within the **TexAns** folder

12. Close all open files

Exercise 86

Sorting and Filtering Summary

1. Open the workbook file from the TexQuest folder named: **bags**

2. Filter the quantity of bags sold to show only records using the font colour green for the value within this field, also filter down to only those records with the brand of Melissa

3. Copy the filtered data and paste, maintaining column widths, commencing at cell A1 of the sheet named: MelissaGreen

4. Clear the previous filter

5. Filter to show records of date within the first quarter period and further filter to show only the top 10 percent values of bags sold and sort ascending by salesroom

6. Copy the data and paste, maintaining column widths, commencing at cell A1 of the sheet named: Top10_Q1

7. Clear the previous filter

8. Filter to show only records whereby the salesperson name does not end with 'n' or begin with 'M' and further filter to show only the records with the Salesroom as Greenock. Sort by most newest date at the top

9. Save the file as a workbook with the file name as: **bags86** within the **TexAns** folder

10. Close all open files

Exercise 87

Remove Duplicates, Split Text and Sort

1.   Open the workbook file from the TexQuest folder named: **workers**

2.   Remove duplicate records from the listing, based upon employee names

3.   Between columns A and B, insert another column, ensuring the continuation of formatting

4.   Replace the contents of cell A4 with: First_Name

5.   Split the full names within column A using an appropriate data tool, to ensure the first name of each employee remains in column A and the surname of each employee moves into the newly created column B

6.   Enter the following text into cell B4: Surname

7.   Sort the records by surname into alphabetical order

8.   Save the file as a workbook with the file name as: **workers87** within the **TexAns** folder

9.   Close all open files

Exercise 88

Inserting a Column Chart

1. Open the workbook file from the TexQuest folder named: **Second2008**

2. Just below the table, insert a 3-D clustered column chart incorporating all the data from July through to December for all the fruits

3. Apply the second available style to the chart

4. Save the file as a workbook with the file name as: **Second2008_88** within the **TexAns** folder

5. Close all open files

Exercise 89

Inserting a Pie Chart

1.　Open the workbook file from the TexQuest folder named: **petty**

2.　Just below the table, insert a pie in 3-D using all sessions for Wednesday

3.　Apply the third available style to the chart

4.　Just below the Wednesday chart, insert an exploded pie using the Morning Session for all days

5.　Apply the second availble layout to the recently inserted chart

6.　Apply chart style of your choice (not the default) to the Morning Session chart

7.　Save the file as a workbook with the file name as: **petty89** within the **TexAns** folder

8.　Close all open files

Exercise 90

Other Charts

1. Open the workbook file from the TexQuest folder named: **Agency**

2. Using all the data for the year, insert a scatter with smooth lines chart immediately below the data

3. Apply style 26 to the scatter chart

4. Underneath the scatter chart, using all the data for the year, insert a stacked line with markers chart

5. Increase the width of the chart to occupy about the same width as the data table itself

6. Apply style 30 to the stacked line chart recently inserted

7. Save the file as a workbook with the file name as: **Agency90** within the **TexAns** folder

8. Close all open files

Exercise 91

Modifying Charts

1. Open the workbook file from the TexQuest folder named: **MonthlySales**

2. Apply a linear forecast trend line to the top monthly total chart

3. Show primary horizontal major gridlines to the top monthly total chart

4. Edit the middle chart for Sydney to show the legend at the top of the chart area

5. Change the middle chart to have the title read as follows: Sydney Sales Chart

6. Edit the Sydney Sales Chart to show data labels centred

7. Adjust the 3D Rotation for the Sydney Sales Chart to now be positioned at 44 degrees perspective

8. Select the bottom chart being the July Sales chart, change the chart type to now be: Doughnut

9. Apply style 26 to the July Sales chart

10. Show the data labels on the July Sales chart

11. Change the colour for the New York segment of the July Sales Chart to now be yellow

12. Save the file as a workbook with the file name as: **MonthlySales91** within the **TexAns** folder

13. Close all open files

Exercise 92

Positioning Charts

1. Open the workbook file from the TexQuest folder named: **Grocery**

2. Move the Banana chart from the Results sheet to the Banana sheet to the right of the list of names, with the top left of the chart commencing at around cell B2 of the Banana sheet

3. Returning to the Results sheet, generate a pie chart for the Salesperson named Collins using that particular record details pertaining to Carrot, Banana and Tomato, with a title of Collins

4. Place the newly created Collins chart into the sheet named: Collins

5. Returning to the Results sheet, Generate a 2-D clustered bar chart for the Salesperson named McStay using that particular record details pertaining to Cabbage, Carrot, Banana and Tomato, with a title of McStay

6. Place the newly created McStay chart into the sheet named: McStay

7. Generate a line with markers chart using all the grocery data for all salespersons, except the Region field, placing the chart on a new dedicated sheet named: AllSales

8. Save the file as a workbook with the file name as: **Grocery92** within the **TexAns** folder

9. Close all open files

Exercise 93

Chart Summary

1. Open the workbook file from the TexQuest folder named: **ticket**

2. Insert a 3-D cylinder column chart underneath the table on the 2010 sheet, using all the data for all countries. Increase the width of the chart to occupy an area in similar width to the data table

3. Apply chart layout 7 to the newly created chart

4. Edit the chart to enable a vertical axis title to read: Values

5. Edit the chart to enable a horizontal axis title to read: Countries

6. Insert a 2-D pie chart covering all values for Nigeria only

7. Edit the Nigeria chart to remove the legend but to centrally show the individual percentage values for each segment with the category name

8. Dislocate the postage segment and move slightly out

9. Move the Nigeria chart to cell C5 on the sheet named: Nigeria

10. Insert a 3D pie chart for all values related to Jordan

11. Move the Jordan chart onto a new sheet specifically for the chart alone, naming the new sheet: JordanChart

12. Save the file as a workbook with the file name as: **ticket93** within the **TexAns** folder

13. Close all open files

Exercise 94

Chart Summary 2

1. Open the workbook file from the TexQuest folder named:
    marriages

2. Insert a scatter with straight lines and markers chart using
    all the available data

3. Apply style 26 to the newly created chart

4. Add an exponential trend line to the chart

5. Apply a gradient fill to the Plot Area of the chart, with
    gradient stops at 33 percent, 44 percent , 55 percent and
    transparency at 10 percent

6. Position the chart at the immediate right hand side of the
    data table

7. Size the chart to: Height of 8.2 cm and Width of 13.7 cm

8. Print 2 copies of the chart only

9. Copy the chart and paste into Sheet2 with the top left hand
    corner sitting around cell D13

10. Return to Sheet1 of the workbook and change the chart
    type on this sheet only to a stacked column 3-D chart

11. Apply style 36 to the edited chart on Sheet1

12. Save the file as a workbook with the file name as:
    marriages94 within the **TexAns** folder

13. Close all open files

Exercise 95

Header and Footer, Print Options and View

1. Open the workbook file from the TexQuest folder named: **seaports**

2. Working with Sheet1 of the workbook, allocate the viewing and printing of gridlines and headings

3. Adjust printing options to fit onto 1 landscape orientated page

4. Ensure the data is positioned centrally vertically and horizontally for printing purposes

5. Add a header, centred, with the following text: Shendmare Consignment Analysis

6. Add a footer with "confidential", the date and sheet or page number

7. Print 2 copies of Sheet1

8. Working with Sheet2, add a centred header with the following text: confirmed and unconfirmed

9. Adjust the printing options to fit onto 1 page wide and 4 pages long with landscape orientation

10. Set the header row A to print on every page to aid the viewing of each page within the print out

11. Print 1 copy of pages 2, 3 and 4 of Sheet2

12. Save the file as a workbook with the file name as: **seaports95** within the **TexAns** folder

13. Close all open files

Exercise 96

Define Named Range

1. Open the workbook file from the TexQuest folder named: **milk**

2. Apply a name of Skimmed to the range of cells: B6:B17 with the scope of Sheet1 only and not across the whole of the workbook, adding the comment to the named range as follows: This is the range of cells for all months from January to December relating to Skimmed Milk only

3. Apply a name of Creamed to the range of cells: D6:D17 with the scope of Sheet1 only and not across the whole of the workbook, adding the comment to the named range as follows: This is the range of cells for all months from January to December relating to all milk not allocated as Skimmed or Semi Skimmed processes

4. Apply a name of Semi to the range of cells: C6:C17 with the scope of the whole workbook and add the comment wording as follows: This is the range of cells for all months from January to December relating to Semi Skimmed Milk

5. Apply a name of January to the range of cells: B6:D6 with the scope of the whole workbook and add the comment wording as follows: January values only for all products

6. Locate the range of cells named Tuesday, changing the cell contents from the current "Monday" to the correct: Tuesday

7. Save the file as a workbook with the file name as: **milk96** within the **TexAns** folder

8. Close all open files

Exercise 97

Create Named Ranges from Selection

1. Open the workbook file from the TexQuest folder named: **fruit**

2. Select cells C5:C25

3. Apply a name to the selected range of cells using the top row

4. Select cells D5:D25

5. Apply a name to the selected range of cells using the top row

6. Select the range of cells known as Banana

7. Select the correct range of cells F6:F25 and name this range as Banana, ensuring the old range known as Banana is no longer allocated

8. Select the range of cells known as Tomato

9. Select the correct range of cells G5:G25 and name this range as Tomato, replacing the old named range of cells

10. Print 1 copy of the range of cells known as Totals

11. Delete the Name of "SelectedOnly" but do not disturb or delete the contents of the actual cells

12. Save the file as a workbook with the file name as: **fruit97** within the **TexAns** folder

13. Close all open files

Exercise 98

Using Named Ranges in Formulae

1. Open the workbook file from the TexQuest folder named: **house**

2. Name cell F6: TaxRate

3. In cell F10, insert a formula calculating the amount of tax using the named cell TaxRate based upon the net total from cell E10

4. Copy this formula down to cells F11 and F12

5. Further copy the tax calculating formula from cell F12 down through ranges: F20:F24 and F32:F34 to enable all tax calculations to be performed using the applicable named cell of TaxRate

6. Edit the rate of tax within the named TaxRate cell to now read: 22%

7. Name the range of cells G10:G12 as SalesElectrical

8. Name the range of cells G20:G24 as SalesNonElectrical

9. Name the range of cells G32:G34 as SalesBedding

10. In cell D40, insert a formula calculating the total sales for all products, using the Named Ranges

11. Save the file as a workbook with the file name as: **house98** within the **TexAns** folder

12. Close all open files

Exercise 99

Formulae referencing to other worksheets

1.   Open the workbook file from the TexQuest folder named:
     footers

2.   In cell B6 of the totals sheet, insert a formula calculating
     the amounts from all levels for the month of January from
     the sheet named: first

3.   Similar to the above, in cell B7 insert a formula calculating
     the amounts from all levels for the month of February from
     the sheet named: first. Continue this operation down
     through the months to June

4.   In cell B12 of the totals sheet, insert a formula calculating
     the amounts from all levels for the month of June from the
     sheet named: second

5.   Similar to the above, within the totals sheet, continue the
     insertion of formulae to calculate each respective month
     from the sheet named: second

6.   Likewise, in cell B23 of the totals sheet, insert a formula
     calculating the amounts from all levels for the month of
     January from the sheet named: ladies1

7.   Continue the insertion of formulae within the Ladies section
     for each respective month within the totals sheet, using the
     values from the ladies1 sheet up to and including June,
     using values from the ladies2 sheet for July to December

8.   Save the file as a workbook with the file name as:
     footers99 within the **TexAns** folder

9.   Close all open files

Exercise 100

Named Ranges Summary

1. Open the workbook file from the TexQuest folder named:
    stockfirst

2. Navigate to the "Italics" named range and format all the
    cells to italics except for the third one down whereby
    contents need to be underlined

3. Edit the range named NorthApr to extend and include all
    cells in the range: E8:E11

4. Navigate to the Total per Region sheet, in cell B7 for the
    January Eastern total, enter a formula using the named
    range of EastJan to calculate the total value

5. Continue throughout the Eastern months and insert
    relevant formulae to calculate totals using the respective
    named ranges: EastFeb, EastMar, EastApr

6. Similarly, insert formulae for each of the regions and each
    month relating thereto. For Western: WestJan, WestFeb,
    WestMar, WestApr. For Nothern: NorthJan, NorthFeb,
    NorthMar, NorthApr

7. Within the Total per Region sheet, cells B7:B9 need to be
    named January, C7:C9 name February, D7:D9 name
    March and lastly E7:E9 to be named April

8. In cell B13, enter a formula using relevant named ranges
    to calculate the grand total of all regions for all months

9. Save the file as a workbook with the file name as:
    stockfirst100 within the **TexAns** folder

10. Close all open files

Exercise 101

Error Correction

1. Open the workbook file from the TexQuest folder named: **audit**

2. Use error correction tools to identify and fix any errors within the workbook

3. Save the file as a workbook with the file name as: **audit101** within the **TexAns** folder

4. Close all open files

Exercise 102

More Error Correction

1. Open the workbook file from the TexQuest folder named: **pcselling**

2. Use error correction tools to identify and fix any errors within the workbook

3. Save the file as a workbook with the file name as: **pcselling102** within the **TexAns** folder

4. Close all open files

Exercise 103

Data Validation

1. Open the workbook file from the TexQuest folder named: **clubba**

2. Using the correct tool, ensure anyone recording a record must input at least 1 character of text into cells A4 and B4, whereby a stop error alert entitled "Insufficient " and explanation within the error message of "More than one character of text is required". No input message is required for these cells

3. Control input into cell C4 to ensure anyone recording a record must insert data of a whole number nature and 21 or over. The cell must not be left blank upon input. An input message is required, entitled "Age restriction applies" and with the message of "The employee must be aged 21 or over". If incorrect data is inserted, a stop error alert must appear entitled "Incorrect age" and error message of "Remember the employee must be 21 or over by law"

4. Input into cell D4 must be a selection from the list within cells A14:A18, with a drop down available for the user to select from, all other defaults should apply

5. Input into cell E4 must be a date within the range of recruitment dates shown in the range of cells: B13:B17

6. Save the file as a workbook with the file name as: **clubba103** within the **TexAns** folder

7. Close all open files

Exercise 104

Skills Assessment 2

1. Open the workbook file from the TexQuest folder named: **invmag**

2. In cell B14, enter a formula to retrieve the relevant Magazine Title from the Magazines sheet based upon the code contained within cell A14 of the Invoice sheet

3. Similarly, in cells B15, B16 and B17, enter formulae to retrieve Magazine Tile data based upon the contents within the respective A15, A16 and A17 cells. Use the table on the Magazines sheet to populate the relevant cells within the Invoice sheet

4. In cell D14 of the Invoice sheet, enter a formula to input the Selling Price based upon the code in cell A14 on the Invoice sheet, retrieving relevant information from the Magazines sheet

5. As above, do likewise for cells D15, D16, D17 and base the retrieval of information upon the codes resident in the respective A15, A16 and A17

6. In cell E21 of the invoice sheet, enter a formula with relevant function to calculate the total amount due based upon the total above this cell

7. Place a top and thick bottom border around cells C21:E21

8. Format cells E21 and B23 of the invoice sheet to show the contents using currency

9. Format cells D6:D8 to use a fill colour of light green

10. In cell D10 of the Invoice sheet, enter a formula with relevant function to insert the current system date

11. In cell B27 of the Invoice sheet, enter a formula to calculate 90 days from the date shown in cell D10

12. In cell B26 of the invoice sheet, enter a formula with relevant function to show either "cheque" or "credit card" depending upon whether the total amount due is more or less than the limit displayed in cell B23

13. Reduce the font size of cell A24 to 8 point but embolden and use italics

14. Delete the sheet named: Unwanted

15. Insert a new sheet named: newlogo

16. Move the newly created sheet named newlogo to between the Packaging and Zed sheets

17. Apply the colour red to the Invoice and Magazine sheet tabs

18. Navigate back to the newlogo sheet and insert a piece of clip art around cell B22 relevant to books or magazines

19. Size the newly inserted clipart to: 1.5 cm wide and 1.7 cm height

20. Navigate to the Magazines sheet and filter based upon the distributors field showing only those records for Zed Books Global and Fandabyydizzit Magazook distributors

21. Copy only the magazine titles from the filtered data and paste into the sheet named: Zed, at cell A4

22. Sort the magazine titles on the zed sheet into reverse alphabetical order

23. Copy the list of magazine titles and selling price from the Invoice sheet and paste into the relevant places within the Packaging sheet, notably commencing at cell A2

24. Sort the magazine titles list within the Packaging sheet into ascending alphabetical order

25. Remaining within the Packaging sheet, apply a name to cell A10 as: packagingrate

26. In cell C2 of the Packaging sheet, insert a formula to calculate the packaging cost based upon the selling price in cell B2 and the named cell packagingrate

27. Replicate the formula from cell C2 down through and including cell C5, ensuring the correct cell references are used for each formula

28. At cell A13 of the Packaging sheet, insert a 3D pie chart for the magazine titles and packaging costs

29. Edit the chart to show the legend at the bottom of the chart area

30. Apply style 22 to the newly created chart

31. Return to the Magazines sheet and clear any filters and ensure the listing is in ascending alphabetical order of Magazine ID

32. Navigate to the Invoice sheet and incorporate a comment to cell B27 as follows: This date is 90 days from the invoice date

33. Save the file as a workbook with the file name as: **invmag104** within the **TexAns** folder

34. Close all open files

Exercise 105

Skills Assessment 3

1. Open the workbook file from the TexQuest folder named: **rent**

2. In cell A20, insert a hyperlink to the e-mail address of info@mahoosinmanagementproperty.com with the diplayed text as "E-mail the helpdesk" and provide a screen tip stating: Click here to send e-mail to the helpdesk of Mahoosin

3. Implement conditional formatting for cells B4:B13 whereby any value is lesser than the amount shown in cell B23 will be displayed with Yellow fill with Dark Yellow Text

4. In cell D4 enter formula with relevant function to calculate whether the date in C4 is earlier than the required payment date shown in cell C23. If the date is earlier then the text "Paid On Time" is to be displayed and if the date is after the required date then the text "Late Payment" is to be displayed

5. Replicate the formula in cell D4 down through all cells in the range D4:D13 ensuring the correct cell references are used

6. In cell B15, enter a formula to calculate the average rent from all the values shown in column B under the rent heading

7. In cell B16, enter a formula to calculate the highest rent from all the values shown in column B under the rent heading

8. In cell B17, enter a formula to calculate the lowest rent from all the values shown in column B under the rent heading

9.   Edit cell C23 to now read: 15 May 2009

10. Insert an arrow shape at cell D23 pointing toward cell D22

11. Merge cells C15 and D15, entering the following text without centre alignment: Payment must be received on time

12. Merge cells E1:E23, entering the following text without centre alignment: Late Payment Monitor

13. Rotate the newly inserted text downward in the merged cell range of E1:E23

14. Increase the font size in cell E1 to 22 point and double underline using font colour of red

15. Insert a centre header with the text: Mahoosin Payment Scheme

16. Print 1 copy of the whole workbook

17. Save the file as a workbook with the file name as: **rent105** within the **TexAns** folder

18. Close all open files

Exercise 106

Skills Assessment 4

1. Open the workbook file from the TexQuest folder named: **Soccer**

2. In cell E28 of the clothing sheet, enter a formula with relevant function, to calculate the discount amount based upon the discounts shown on the discount worksheet within the soccer workbook

3. Cells E27:E29 of the clothing sheet require formatting for currency

4. Navigate to the equipment sheet, in cell E28, enter a formula with relevant function, to calculate the discount amount based upon the discounts shown on the discount worksheet

5. Cells E27:E29 of the clothing sheet require formatting for currency

6. Navigate to the totals worksheet, in cell B7 enter a formula to calculate the total after discount from the clothing sheet plus the total after discount from the equipment sheet

7. Format cell B7 within the totals worksheet for accounting as opposed to currency formatting

8. In cell E33 of the clothing sheet, enter a formula to calculate 30 days from the Invoice date

9. Edit the comments associated with cell E33 of the clothing sheet to now read: 30 days credit provided

10. In cell E33 of the equipment sheet, enter a formula to calculate 90 days from the Invoice date appearing on this sheet

11. Add a comment to cell E33 of the equipment sheet, to read: 90 days rather than the usual 30 days credit for this invoice due to equipment delivery schedule

12. Set the print area covering A14:E29 for the clothing sheet

13. Change the page orientation for the clothing sheet to landscape

14. Adjust the scaling to 115 percent of actual size for printing purposes of the clothing sheet

15. Centre the clothing sheet vertically and horizontally for printing purposes

16. Print 2 copies of the print area of the clothing sheet in black and white

17. Save the file as a workbook with the file name as: **Soccer106** within the **TexAns** folder

18. Close all open files

Exercise 107

Assessment 5

1.   Request a brand new workbook

2.   Commencing with cell B5, ensuring each value is identified in the adjacent cell, plot out calculations and use a formula with relevant function for monthly payments of a £530,000 loan over 5 years at the constant interest rate of 7.2 percent per annum, with payments being made at the beginning of every month and a balance of £20,500 at the end of the loan period

3.   Format percentage cells appropriately

4.   Format currency cells appropriately

5.   Format the monthly payments in the colour red for negative values in accordance with standard currency formatting of cells

6.   Save the file as a workbook with the file name as: **loan107** within the **TexAns** folder

7.   Close all open files

Exercise 108

Skills Assessment 6

1.   Open the workbook file from the TexQuest folder named: **patients**

2.   Navigate to the patients sheet within the patients workbook

3.   Make all columns 15 points or 125 pixels wide

4.   Delete the top empty row

5.   Insert a row after row 9

6.   Input the following data: FirstName of Karine, Surname of Patel, Age of 55, Sex of Female, Town of Philadelphia, Doctor of Drummond

7.   Two duplicate records exist in error, delete these records only

8.   Locate the record with the Surname beginning with the second and third letters being "jo" and make the whole record red font

9.   Change any reference of the town Paris and make it Melbourne

10. Centre align all contents within column C

11. Filter the list to show records for the doctor name of Chan with the town as Copenhagen

12. Copy the filtered date and paste into the sheet named chan with headings for each column, maintaining all column width of 15 point (125 pixels)

13. Return to the patients sheet and clear filters

14. Filter the list in the patients sheet to show records for the

doctor name of Drummond with the town as Berlin

15. Copy the filtered data and paste into the sheet named Drummond with headings for each column, maintaining all column width of 15 point (125 pixels)

16. Return to the patients sheet and clear filters

17. Filter the list to show records of all patients between the ages of 40 and 60

18. Sort the filtered list in ascending alphabetical order by Surname

19. Save the file as a workbook with the file name as: **patients108** within the **TexAns** folder

20. Close all open files

Exercise 109

Skills Assessment 7

1. Open the workbook file from the TexQuest folder named: **lines**

2. Freeze the header row

3. Scroll down to row 55

4. Select rows 55, 56 and 57, making all the contents in the rows bold

5. Hide the gridlines

6. Save the file as a workbook with the file name as: **lines109** within the **TexAns** folder

7. Close all open files

Other titles by Mark Gillan

Available from all major book retailers worldwide

Microsoft Word – Exercises with Video Training on DVD-ROM
ISBN: 978 0955777028

Teacher presents Web Design – HTML and CSS
ISBN: 978 0955777059
(Also available on Kindle)

More books to follow soon

www.iDistanceLearn.com

Exercise List for reference:

Useful websites:

www.SkooshMedia.com

www.iDistanceLearn.com

www.ArtSale2.com

www.MarkGillan.com

www.Photographer2.com

www.StopSmoking2.com

www.Hypnotism2.com

www.CanvasPrintsSale.com

www.Ebook-Ebook.com

www.JockTheArtist.com

www.ExcelExercises.com